Second Grade Dictionary S

MW00810935

Table of Contents

Introduction

When a child asks you how to spell a word or what it means, what do you do? Do you give the child the answers? Or do you tell the child to look in a dictionary? If you are a parent, giving your child the answers may seem like the kind thing to do. Sometimes it is the easier thing to do. But learning the skills required to use a dictionary, even for young children and students, is essential to their becoming independent readers.

Students remember what they read better than what they are told. Finding a word in the dictionary will reinforce the word, its spelling, and its meaning in a student's mind. Simply writing the letters as someone else dictates them does not offer the same opportunity for reinforcement.

Dictionary skills are also useful across the curriculum and in real-life situations. Learning how to find words by sounding them out and using alphabetical order helps students to use indexes, glossaries, encyclopedias, phone books, and other reference books. Looking up meanings and choosing the correct meaning of an unknown word through context help a student to become an independent reader in all subjects.

Use

Second Grade Dictionary Skills is designed to supplement the language arts curriculum. However, many pages concentrate on other areas of the curriculum, such as science, art, health and PE, math, and social studies. There are icons on these pages to help the teacher integrate *Dictionary Skills* into these areas.

At the second-grade level, the skills required to use a dictionary are introduced, and the students are given the opportunity for practice. The units, Alphabetical Order, Parts of Speech, Multiple Meanings, and Using a Dictionary, are meant to ease young students into the practice of using a dictionary independently. A dictionary designed for young readers is recommended as a companion to this workbook.

Most pages introduce a topic with examples and then provide practice. Some pages include a section called "Take Another Step," which encourages students to apply what they have learned.

The Glossary on page 3 is meant to help the teacher and the students as they use this book. The Dictionary Page Diagram on page 4 can be enlarged, laminated, copied, or simply posted in an area for easy reference. The Assessment on pages 5–6 can be used as a pretest and/or a posttest to gauge learning.

It is hoped that students will have fun while learning their new dictionary skills. Fun titles and topics of interest are meant to engage young students in learning. Devote part of a bulletin board to dictionary skills and display students' work. Encourage discussions and the use of the dictionary whenever the opportunity presents itself. Most of all, have fun!

Glossary

adjective (adj.) a word that describes a noun.

adverb (adv.) a word that describes a verb or an adjective.

alphabetical order in the order of the alphabet; ordered from A to Z.

contraction (contr.) two words written as one, usually with an apostrophe in place of the missing letters.

definition the meaning of a word.

dictionary a book of words in alphabetical order that shows how to spell the words and tells their meanings.

entry word a word defined in a dictionary.

guide words words printed at the top of a page in a dictionary; usually the first and last entry words on that page.

noun (n.) a word that is a person, place, or thing.

part of speech a group of words in a language to which a word can be added; a class of words.

prefix a group of letters added to the beginning of a root word to change its meaning.

pronoun (pron.) a word that takes the place of another noun or a group of nouns.

pronunciation guide phonetic spellings to help readers pronounce words.

root word a word to which a prefix or suffix can be added to change its meaning.

suffix a group of letters added to the end of a root word to change its meaning.

verb (v.) a word that shows action.

Dictionary Page Diagram

entry words
words that are defined

guide words
first and last entry words on a page

numbers to show different words with same spelling

example sentence
helps explain meaning

pronunciation guide helps reader to pronounce words

definition
meaning of a word

letter or letters to show part of speech

numbers to show different meanings

page number
number of page in dictionary

---

click/code

clog[1] **v.** to block. Please don't clog the drain.

clog[2] **n.** a heavy, wooden shoe.

close[1] (rhymes with dose) **adj.** 1. near. 2. having a strong bond with someone. I am close to my best friend. 3. with little difference between two things. It was a close race. 4. careful. Take a close look. 5. warm and stuffy.

close[2] (rhymes with nose) **v.** 1. to shut 2. to end. The day came to a close.

cloud n. a mass of water droplets in the sky; usually gray or white.

51

Show What You Know

Directions: Look at the sample dictionary page. Use the sample to answer the questions.

---

maid/maze

mail n. letters and packages sent from one person to another.

make[1] v. 1. to create something. 2. to cause something to happen. I make my sister angry. 3. to do something. Let's make a cake. 4. to add up to. One and one make two.

make[2] n. a type or kind. What make is your car?

mall n. a shopping center.

---

1. What are the guide words on this page? _____

2. How many entry words are on this page? _____

3. What part of speech is <u>make</u> when it means "to create something"? _____

4. Write one of the example sentences from the sample. _____

_____

5. Which word means "to add up to"? _____

6. Which word shows more than one meaning? _____

7. What is meaning 2 of <u>make[1]</u>? _____

8. What part of speech is <u>mall</u>? _____

☞Go on to the next page.

Show What You Know, p. 2

Directions: Use a dictionary to answer these questions.

9. Find the word <u>mold</u> in the dictionary. What page is it on? _____

10. What are the guide words on the page? _____

11. How many entry words are there for <u>mold</u>? _____

12. How many meanings are there for <u>mold</u> as a noun? _____

13. What is meaning 1 for <u>mold</u> as a noun? _____

_____

14. What is meaning 2 for <u>mold</u> as a noun? _____

_____

15. What is the meaning for <u>mold</u> as a verb? _____

_____

16. Write an example sentence for one meaning of <u>mold</u>. _____

_____

_____

Name _____ Date _____

A B C Order

a b c d e f g h i j k l m n o p q r s t u v w x y z

How do you put words in ABC order? Look at the first letter of each word. Which letter comes first in the alphabet?

<u>c</u>at   <u>b</u>oy   <u>d</u>og   <u>a</u>nt

Since **a** comes before **b**, **c**, or **d**, **ant** is the first word in this group.

Which letter comes next? Write the words in alphabetical order.

ant   _____   _____   _____

Directions: Look at this list of words. Write them in alphabetical order. Use the alphabet at the top of the page. Cross out each word as you write it.

pot	goat	cap	apple	wing	man
soup	tag	key	boat	zebra	hat

1. _____   5. _____   9. _____

2. _____   6. _____   10. _____

3. _____   7. _____   11. _____

4. _____   8. _____   12. _____

Unit One: Alphabetical Order:
Introducing Alphabetical Order
Dictionary Skills 2, SV 2721-9

Name _____ Date _____

Sport Order

How do you put words in alphabetical order when the beginning letters are the same?

Look at the words **skate** and **stick**. Which word would be first? The first letter, **s**, is the same. You have to look at the second letter. The second letter of **skate** is **k**. The second letter of **stick** is **t**. The letter **k** comes before the letter **t**, so the word **skate** comes before the word **stick**.

Directions: Look at these names of different sports. The first letters are the same. Circle the word that would come first in each pair.

1. hockey	2. bowling	3. skating	4 tubing
hiking	baseball	swimming	tennis

5. basketball	6. climbing	7. skiing	8. football
boating	canoeing	sliding	flying

 Take Another Step

Write three of your favorite games or sports. Then write **1**, **2**, and **3** above the words to show ABC order.

_____

_____

Down on the Farm

What if the first two letters of some words are the same? Then, you must look at the third letter to see which word comes first. Look at these words.

horse

honey

hog

Each word begins with **ho**. The third letter in **ho<u>r</u>se** is **<u>r</u>**. The third letter in **ho<u>n</u>ey** is **<u>n</u>**. The third letter in **ho<u>g</u>** is **<u>g</u>**. So the alphabetical order of these words is **hog**, **honey**, **horse**.

Directions: Look at each group of words. Put them in the correct alphabetical order. Write them on the lines.

1. barn _____
   basket _____
   baby _____

4. hay _____
   hat _____
   happy _____

2. cart _____
   cat _____
   call _____

5. chicken _____
   chore _____
   chain _____

3. peas _____
   pens _____
   pets _____

6. hog _____
   hoe _____
   home _____

Name _____   Date _____

Alphabet Soup

Directions: Put the words in the correct bowl of soup.
Then, write <u>1</u>, <u>2</u>, and <u>3</u> to put each bowl of words in correct
alphabetical order.

pea	salt	mushroom	potato	bean	beef
carrot	milk	spice	pasta	barley	tomato
thyme	meat	celery	corn	sausage	taste

_____   _____   _____

_____   _____   _____

_____   _____   _____

_____   _____   _____

_____   _____   _____

_____   _____   _____

Unit One: Alphabetical Order:
Putting It All Together
Dictionary Skills 2, SV 2721-9

Word Race

Directions: Look at the words below. Write them in ABC order on the race track.

year	lady
yet	fool
joke	trot
bell	dollar
donkey	alike
travel	foot
beaver	wag
net	joy
half	nest
hall	wave
alley	ladder

FINISH

1. _____ 12. _____
2. _____ 13. _____
3. _____ 14. _____
4. _____ 15. _____
5. _____ 16. _____
6. _____ 17. _____
7. _____ 18. _____
8. _____ 19. _____
9. _____ 20. _____
10. _____ 21. _____
11. _____ 22. _____

Take Another Step

Write your first name on the chalkboard. All of your classmates will write their name, too. Then, at your seat, write all of the names in ABC order.

State Scramble

Directions: ▶ Here is an ABC challenge! Use your scissors to cut along the lines. Then, paste all of the states in ABC order on another piece of paper.

Here are some hints to help you.
- Make piles of states that begin with the same letter.
- Put each pile in ABC order before you begin to paste.
- If the first word of two states is the same, look at the second word.

Texas	California	New Mexico	North Dakota
Georgia	Hawaii	Kansas	Missouri
Oregon	Maine	Wyoming	New York
Florida	Iowa	New Jersey	Nevada
Nebraska	Montana	Utah	Kentucky
Michigan	Alabama	Alaska	Massachusetts
Arizona	Colorado	Delaware	Connecticut
Louisiana	Arkansas	Idaho	Illinois
Indiana	Wisconsin	Vermont	New Hampshire
Ohio	Oklahoma	Washington	Rhode Island
Tennessee	West Virginia	Minnesota	South Carolina
Maryland	Mississippi	South Dakota	Pennsylvania
North Carolina	Virginia		

Name _____ Date _____

How Does Your Garden Grow?

A **noun** is a word that names a person, place, or thing.

That **plant** has one **flower**.

A noun can tell about more than one person, place, or thing. Add **s** to most nouns to make them mean "more than one."

The other **plants** have many **flowers**.

Directions:▶ Choose and circle the correct nouns.

1. Mary plants (seed, seeds) in her garden.

2. She wants to grow many (flower, flowers).

3. Mary keeps (weed, weeds) out of the garden.

4. She puts (water, waters) on her seeds.

5. Mary waits for her (flower, flowers) to grow.

6. Soon, tiny (shoot, shoots) show.

7. Then, the (stem, stems) grow tall.

8. Each stem grows a (bud, buds).

9. The bud blossoms into a pretty (flower, flowers).

10. Mary has a beautiful (garden, gardens).

Directions:▶ Find other nouns in the sentences. The nouns will be a person, place, or thing. Circle them.

Happy Hamsters

A **pronoun** is a word that takes the place of one or more nouns.

Tina and James have hamsters.

They have hamsters.

The pronouns **I**, **we**, **he**, **she**, **it**, and **they** are used in the naming part of a sentence.

The hamster ate some food.

It ate some food.

Directions: Read each sentence. Think of a pronoun to take the place of the underlined words. Write the pronoun on the line.

1. <u>Tina's hamster</u> lives in a cage. _____

2. <u>Tina</u> feeds her hamster every day. _____

3. Tina gives <u>her hamster</u> water, too. _____

4. <u>The hamster</u> needs a clean cage. _____

5. <u>Tina</u> has a brother named James. _____

6. <u>James</u> has a hamster, too. _____

7. <u>Tina and James</u> like to play with their hamsters. _____

8. <u>My friend and I</u> went to visit Tina and James. _____

9. <u>Tina and James</u> let us hold the hamsters. _____

10. <u>The hamsters</u> were very cute and soft. _____

Name _____ Date _____

Take a Trip

A **verb** is a word that shows action.

People **drive** across the country.

We **walk** to school.

Directions: Read each sentence. Choose a verb from the box to complete each sentence. Use each word one time.

| lands | lives | sleep | walk | hugs | eat | fly | take | smiles | ride |

1. My aunt _____ very far away.

2. We have to _____ to her house.

3. We _____ a plane.

4. The plane _____ in a big city near my aunt's town.

5. We _____ in a taxi to her street.

6. My aunt _____ when she sees us.

7. She _____ everyone.

8. We _____ at a restaurant near her house.

9. We can _____ to it.

10. We _____ well after a busy day!

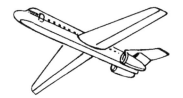

Take Another Step

Write five verbs that tell what you do each day.

_____

_____

Name _____ Date _____

At the Zoo

An **adjective** is a word that describes other words.
An adjective can tell about feelings.

That seal looks **happy**.

An adjective can tell how many.

There are **many** animals in the zoo.

Directions: Read each sentence. Circle all of the words that describe other words. They will tell about feelings, colors, numbers, or size.

1. The zoo is home to many animals.
2. We spent two long hours there.
3. We saw three huge elephants.
4. We saw four wild tigers.
5. There were five green parrots.
6. Six striped zebras ate grass.
7. We fed seven tall giraffes.
8. Eight slow turtles sat near a pond.
9. Nine silly monkeys were in the trees.
10. When it was time to leave, we were ten happy, tired people!

 Take Another Step

Write five adjectives that describe you!

_____

_____

Name _____ Date _____

Short Cuts

A **contraction** is a way to put two words together.

is + not = isn't

An **apostrophe** (') takes the place of one or more letters.

are + not = aren't   was + not = wasn't
have + not = haven't   were + not = weren't
has + not = hasn't   had + not = hadn't
can + not = can't   did + not = didn't
do + not = don't   is + not = isn't

Directions: ⟩ Read each sentence. Choose a contraction to use in place of the underlined words. Write the contraction on the line.

1. Bob <u>does not</u> want to run. _____

2. He <u>is not</u> fond of exercise. _____

3. Bob <u>has not</u> been riding his bike. _____

4. Bob's legs <u>have not</u> gotten stronger. _____

5. Bob <u>can not</u> be healthy without exercise. _____

6. Bob <u>was not</u> always this way. _____

7. Bob's mom and dad <u>are not</u> happy. _____

8. Bob's mom and dad <u>do not</u> like what they see. _____

9. Suddenly, Bob <u>is not</u> lazy anymore. _____

10. Now he <u>can not</u> stop running and jumping! _____

Adding On

Some words can be broken into parts.
A **prefix** is added to the beginning of a word
to change its meaning.

Sue is happy.   Sue is **un**happy.

A **suffix** is added to the end of a word to change its meaning.

Don is help**ful**.   Don is help**less**.

The part of the word that a prefix or suffix is added to is called
a **root word**.

<u>help</u>ful   un**<u>happy</u>**

Directions: ▶ Read each sentence. Look at the word in dark
print. Circle the prefix or suffix. Underline the root word.
Write <u>prefix</u> or <u>suffix</u> after the sentence to tell what you circled.

1. Jill is **hopeful** that she will win. _____

2. The broken swing was **useless**. _____

3. Dee is **unable** to come. _____

4. That glass is **breakable**. _____

5. This baby bird is **helpless**. _____

Unit Two: Parts of Speech:
Recognizing Prefixes, Suffixes, and Root Words
Dictionary Skills 2, SV 2721-9

Name _____   Date _____

Change the Meaning

Here are some common prefixes and suffixes and what they mean.

Prefix	Meaning
un-	not
re-	again

Suffix	Meaning
-ful	full of
-less	without
-able	able to be

Directions: Read the sentences. Underline the words with a prefix or a suffix. Tell what the words mean. The first one is done for you.

1. The child is <u>unable</u> to reach the jar. __not able_____

2. I will rewind the film. _____

3. My sister is unhappy. _____

4. Try to reheat your dinner. _____

5. Those flowers are beautiful. _____

6. The room was a hopeless mess. _____

7. I hope your shirt is washable. _____

8. Be careful with those dishes. _____

9. I need to refill my gas tank. _____

10. That was a thoughtless thing to do. _____

Now You Know

- A **noun** names a person, place, or thing.   (cat, Joe)
- A **pronoun** takes the place of a noun.   (it, she)
- A **verb** shows action.   (run, drive)
- An **adjective** describes a noun.   (two, green)
- A **contraction** is two words joined together.   (it's, can't)
- A **prefix** or a **suffix** is added onto a **root word**
  to change its meaning.   (helpful, helpless)

Directions: Read each sentence below. Then, read the part of speech at the end of the sentence. In the space, add a word that matches the part of speech. The first one is done for you.

1. Tony _____ran_____ to the park.   **verb**

2. I _____ want to go to bed yet.   **contraction**

3. _____ are my brothers.   **pronoun**

4. Look at that _____ baby.   **adjective**

5. Add this to your _____ collection.   **noun**

6. She was care _____, so she broke her glasses.   **suffix**

7. We need to _____ turn that book to the library.   **prefix**

8. I think I _____ my favorite hat.   **verb**

9. I have never seen such a _____ tree!   **adjective**

10. I can not un _____ this knot.   **root word**

What Does It Mean?

- -

Directions: Some words have more than one meaning. Look at each pair of pictures. Read each sentence. Then write the letter of the correct meaning on the line.

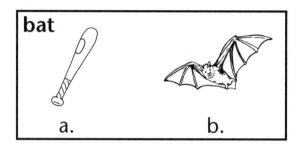

1. _____ Tony has a wooden bat.

2. _____ The bat sleeps during the day.

3. _____ The pitcher threw the ball.

4. _____ The milk pitcher is empty.

5. _____ Kendra wants to plant a tree.

6. _____ Jody grew a plant at school.

7. _____ The puppy is light.

8. _____ Please turn on a light.

Art Smart

Directions: Read each sentence. Then, draw a picture to show what the word in dark print means.

1. Some birds **fly** south in the winter.

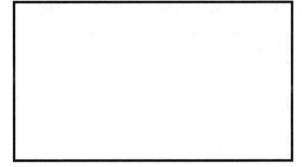

2. There is a **fly** on the wall.

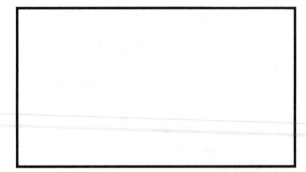

3. Please **set** the table.

4. Mia has a new **set** of paints.

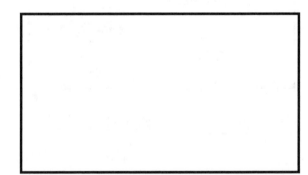

Pet or Pet?

In a dictionary, words with more than one meaning look like this example. Each meaning has a number.

pet   **1.** animal kept as a friend. **2.** to stroke.

Michelle has a **pet** turtle. (meaning 1)
Meli loves to **pet** his puppy. (meaning 2)

Directions: ▶ Read the meanings of each word. Then, choose the correct meaning for each word in dark print in the sentences. Write the number of the meaning you choose on the line.

cold   1. not warm. 2. a sickness of the nose and throat.

tie   1. to fasten together with string. 2. a cloth worn around the neck.

wave   1. moving water. 2. to move the hand back and forth as a greeting.

1. Please wear a **tie** to the show. _____

2. **Wave** good-bye to your friends. _____

3. Jane has a bad **cold**. _____

4. A big **wave** got me wet at the beach. _____

5. It is **cold** and snowy outside. _____

6. David needs help to **tie** his shoes. _____

The Trouble with Trunks

Some words have many meanings. Look at the different meanings for the word **trunk**.

trunk   1. the main stem of a tree. 2. the main part of your body, not including your head, arms, or legs. 3. a large box for storage. 4. the nose of an elephant. 5. storage space in a car.

Directions: For each sentence, choose the correct meaning. Write the number of the meaning you choose in the space. Underline the words in each sentence that give you clues to the meaning.

1. Lori's **trunk** is longer than Sam's is, so she is taller. _____

2. Be sure to close the **trunk** before you drive away. _____

3. That elephant blew water from its **trunk**. _____

4. Let's try to reach around the **trunk** of this tree. _____

5. The car's spare tire is in the **trunk**. _____

6. I think my old toys are in a **trunk** in the attic. _____

7. The elephant uses its **trunk** to lift things. _____

8. The wind broke the **trunk** of that tree. _____

9. Your heart is in the **trunk** of your body. _____

10. Try to slide that **trunk** under the bed. _____

Take Another Step

Think of two meanings for the word **trip**. Draw a picture to show each meaning. Use another piece of paper or the back of this page.

Name _____ Date _____

Guide Words

How do you find a word in a dictionary? First, you must remember to use ABC order. Then, you need to use **guide words**. Guide words are found at the top of each page in a dictionary. They tell you which words can be found on that page.

Here is an example: **spot/stamp**

The first word on this page will be <u>spot</u>. The last word on this page will be <u>stamp</u>. All of the other words on this page will come <u>between</u> <u>spot</u> and <u>stamp</u> in ABC order.

Would you find the word <u>**stack**</u> on this page? Yes. <u>**Stack**</u> comes <u>between</u> <u>spot</u> and <u>stamp</u> in ABC order.

Would you find the words <u>**swing**</u> or <u>**spill**</u> on this page? No. <u>**Swing**</u> comes <u>after</u> <u>stamp</u> in ABC order. <u>**Spill**</u> comes <u>before</u> <u>spot</u>.

Directions: Look at the guide words. Circle the words that would be on a page with the guide words. Draw a line through the words that would not be on the page.

1. dragon/dump

dress	dune
drop	drape
dad	drip
dime	drum

2. harm/heel

harp	head
ham	heavy
heart	hay
heap	how

Guide Word Practice

Look at these guide words.

 **baby/bed**

1. What is the first entry word on this dictionary page? _____

2. What is the last entry word on this dictionary page? _____

3. Which of these words could be found on this dictionary page? Circle them.

   bad   bud   bid   bone   bend   bar   back

Directions: Choose the pair of guide words that you would use to find each word. The first one is done for you.

bat/boy	fit/fun	race/run	see/sit

4. sent ___see/sit___   8. sheep _____

5. bath _____   9. flag _____

6. room _____   10. ranch _____

7. four _____   11. big _____

 Take Another Step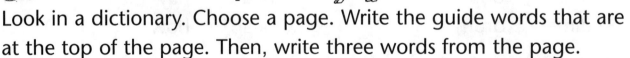

Look in a dictionary. Choose a page. Write the guide words that are at the top of the page. Then, write three words from the page.

Guide Words: _____

Words on the Page: _____

Name _____ Date _____

Finding Words

Guide words help you find the right page of a dictionary. To find the word you are looking for, you must look at **entry words**.

Entry words are in **dark print** in the dictionary. Entry words are in ABC order. Look at this example page.

253

tiny/total

    ti•ny   very small.

    toad   a small animal that is like a frog.

    to•day this day.

    top•ic a subject in writing

Directions: Use the example dictionary page. Answer these questions.

1. Which entry word comes second on the page? _____

2. Which entry word tells about an animal? _____

3. What does <u>today</u> mean? _____

4. What entry word means "very small"? _____

5. Could the entry word <u>tow</u> be on this page? Why or why not?

_____

_____

Unit Four: Using a Dictionary:
Using Entry Words
Dictionary Skills 2, SV 2721-9

Name _____   Date _____

Many Meanings

Many words in the dictionary have more than one meaning. If a word has more than one meaning, each meaning has a number. A dictionary may have sentences to show how to use each meaning. It also tells the part of speech, such as **noun**, that a word is. The part of speech is shown by a letter or a group of letters.

noun = **n.**   adverb = **adv.**

verb = **v.**   contraction = **contr.**

adjective = **adj.**   pronoun = **pron.**

bump¹	**v.** 1. to hit against.
bump²	**n.** 1. a part that sticks out.
burst	**v.** 1. to break apart suddenly. <u>The balloon burst</u>.
	2. to give way to a strong feeling. <u>We burst into laughter</u>.

Directions: Use the dictionary entries. Answer the questions.

1. What word can mean "to break apart"? _____

2. What part of speech is <u>burst</u>? _____

3. Which meaning of <u>bump</u> is used in this sentence—meaning 1

or meaning 2? _____

Don't **bump** your head on the door.

4. Write a sentence for <u>bump</u>, using it as a noun. _____

_____

 Take Another Step

Find the word <u>mine</u> in a dictionary. How many meanings do you find? Write them on another piece of paper.

Unit Four: Using a Dictionary:
Choosing Correct Meanings
Dictionary Skills 2, SV 2721-9

Name _____ Date _____

Body Business

A dictionary

- has guide words to show which words are on a page.
- has entry words in ABC order.
- shows how to spell words.
- tells all of the meanings of a word.
- tells what parts of speech a word can be.
- sometimes gives examples of words in sentences.

Directions: Look at the example. Do what numbers 1–5 tell you to do.

---

blank/boss

blood	**n.** the red liquid that flows through the body.
body	**n.** 1. the whole of a person or an animal. 2. the main part of a thing such as a car.
bone	**n.** one of the hard, white parts that make up the body's skeleton.
bore	**v.** to cause boredom. <u>Bill could bore anyone</u>.

---

1. Circle the guide words with red.

2. Underline the entry words in orange.

3. Circle the example sentence in green.

4. Put a blue **X** on the word that is a verb.

5. Draw a yellow line through meaning 1 of <u>body</u>.

**Unit Four: Using a Dictionary:
Putting It All Together**
Dictionary Skills 2, SV 2721-9

The Meaning of Math

Directions: Use a dictionary to find the words in the chart. Fill in the chart with the information from the dictionary.

Word	Guide Words	Part of Speech	Meaning(s)
add			
count			
math			
number			
set			
sign			

 Take Another Step

Write a sentence to show the meaning of one of the words above.

_____

Second Grade Dictionary Skills
Answer Key

Assessment

Pp. 5–6

1. maid, maze
2. 4
3. verb
4. any sentence: e.g., I make my sister cry.
5. make (as a verb)
6. make (as a verb)
7. to cause something to happen
8. noun

For questions 9–16, answers will vary according to the dictionary used. Check students' answers.

P. 7

Sample:
ant, boy, cat, dog
1. apple
2. boat
3. cap
4. goat
5. hat
6. key
7. man
8. pot
9. soup
10. tag
11. wing
12. zebra

P. 8

1. hiking
2. baseball
3. skating
4. tennis
5. basketball
6. canoeing
7. skiing
8. flying

P. 9

1. baby, barn, basket
2. call, cart, cat
3. peas, pens, pets
4. happy, hat, hay
5. chain, chicken, chore
6. hoe, hog, home

P. 10

Bowl B:
barley, bean, beef
Bowl C:
carrot, celery, corn
Bowl M:
meat, milk, mushroom
Bowl P:
pasta, pea, potato
Bowl S:
salt, sausage, spice
Bowl T:
taste, thyme, tomato

P. 11

1. alike
2. alley
3. beaver
4. bell
5. dollar
6. donkey
7. fool
8. foot
9. half
10. hall
11. joke
12. joy
13. ladder
14. lady
15. nest
16. net
17. travel,
18. trot
19. wag
20. wave
21. year
22. yet

P. 12

1. Alabama
2. Alaska
3. Arizona
4. Arkansas
5. California
6. Colorado
7. Connecticut
8. Delaware
9. Florida
10. Georgia
11. Hawaii
12. Idaho
13. Illinois
14. Indiana
15. Iowa
16. Kansas
17. Kentucky
18. Louisiana
19. Maine
20. Maryland
21. Massachusetts
22. Michigan
23. Minnesota
24. Mississippi
25. Missouri
26. Montana
27. Nebraska
28. Nevada
29. New Hampshire
30. New Jersey
31. New Mexico
32. New York
33. North Carolina
34. North Dakota
35. Ohio
36. Oklahoma
37. Oregon
38. Pennsylvania
39. Rhode Island
40. South Carolina
41. South Dakota
42. Tennessee
43. Texas
44. Utah
45. Vermont
46. Virginia
47. Washington
48. West Virginia
49. Wisconsin
50. Wyoming

P. 13

1. seeds
2. flowers
3. weeds
4. water
5. flowers
6. shoots
7. stems
8. bud
9. flower
10. garden
Other nouns:
1. Mary, garden
2. She (pronoun)
3. Mary, garden
4. She (pronoun), seeds
5. Mary
6. none
7. none
8. stem
9. bud
10. Mary

P. 14

1. It
2. She
3. it
4. It
5. She
6. He
7. They
8. We
9. They
10. They

P. 15

Some words fit into more than one sentence, but best choices follow:

1. lives
2. fly
3. take
4. lands
5. ride
6. smiles
7. hugs
8. eat
9. walk
10. sleep

P. 16

1. many
2. two, long
3. three, huge
4. four, wild
5. five, green
6. Six, striped
7. seven, tall
8. Eight, slow
9. Nine, silly
10. ten, happy, tired

P. 17

1. doesn't
2. isn't
3. hasn't
4. haven't
5. can't
6. wasn't
7. aren't
8. don't
9. isn't
10. can't

P. 18

1. circle <u>ful</u>; underline <u>hope</u>; suffix
2. circle <u>less</u>; underline <u>use</u>; suffix
3. circle <u>un</u>; underline <u>able</u>; prefix
4. circle <u>able</u>; underline <u>break</u>; suffix
5. circle <u>less</u>; underline <u>help</u>; suffix

P. 19

2. rewind; wind again
3. unhappy; not happy
4. reheat; heat again
5. beautiful; full of beauty
6. hopeless; without hope
7. washable; able to be washed
8. careful; full of care
9. refill; fill again
10. thoughtless; without thought

P. 20

Answers may vary.
2. don't
3. They
4. cute
5. coin
6. less
7. re
8. lost
9. tall
10. tie

P. 21

1. a
2. b
3. b
4. a
5. a
6. b
7. b
8. a

P. 22

Check students' work.

P. 23

1. 2
2. 2
3. 2
4. 1
5. 1
6. 1

P. 24

Underlined words may vary. Check students' work.
1. 2
2. 5
3. 4
4. 1
5. 5
6. 3
7. 4
8. 1
9. 2
10. 3

P. 25

1. Circle dress, drop, drape, drip, drum; draw a line through dad, dime, dune
2. Circle harp, heart, heap, head, heavy, hay; draw a line through ham, how

P. 26

1. baby
2. bed
3. bad, bar, back
5. bat/boy
6. race/run
7. fit/fun
8. see/sit
9. fit/fun
10. race/run
11. bat/boy

P. 27

1. toad
2. toad
3. this day
4. tiny
5. No. Tow comes after total in ABC order.

P. 28

1. burst
2. verb

3. Meaning 1
4. Answers will vary.

P. 29

1. Circle <u>blank/boss</u> in red.
2. Underline <u>blood</u>, <u>body</u>, <u>bone</u>, and <u>bore</u> in orange.
3. Circle "Bill could bore anyone." in green.
4. Put a blue X on <u>bore</u>.
5. Draw a yellow line through "the whole of a person or an animal."

P. 30

Answers will vary. Check students' charts.